LEARN TO
SPELL

Walter D. Wright

JAMES NISBET & CO. LTD
DIGSWELL PLACE

Contents

Published by James Nisbet & Co. Ltd, Digswell Place, Welwyn Garden City, Herts
First published 1975   This printing 1976   © James Nisbet   0 7202 0930 7
Made and printed in Great Britain by William Clowes & Sons, Limited
London, Beccles and Colchester

For Better Spelling

1. Always have a dictionary handy when you are writing.
2. Know the alphabet thoroughly so that you can use the dictionary quickly.
3. Keep an alphabetical notebook in which you can write and revise troublesome words.
4. Write smoothly and neatly. Dot your i's and cross your t's. You are more likely to make mistakes if you are untidy, very slow, or if you print in block capitals.
5. If a word has more than one syllable, say it and spell it aloud, syllable by syllable. (For example, en-joy-ment.)
6. If you can see things clearly in your mind's eye, look closely at new words and 'photograph' them so that you can see them with your eyes shut.
7. Pay most attention to the many words that obey spelling rules. Learn the exceptions when you need them.
8. Play word games, do crossword puzzles, and have spelling competitions with your friends.
9. Make up nonsense rhymes or phrases to remember the spellings of tricky words. (For example, Possesses possesses five s's.)
10. It is not enough to know how a word is spelt. Find out how it is pronounced, what it means, and how it is used.

In exercises like those on page 5 you are bound to get the right answers if you build words according to the instructions. In other exercises you may not be sure whether you have spelt words correctly. Use the list at the back of the book to check them.

Words You Must Understand

To be able to follow spelling rules you need to understand words that are used in them. Here are the important ones.

Accent: The word morning is pronounced with more weight or stress on the first part than on the second. This extra stress is called accent. In dictionaries the mark ' is usually placed after the stressed syllable, e.g. for-get'.

Apostrophe: A sign like a raised comma to show that a letter (or letters) has been left out, e.g. don't for do not. It is also used to show possession, e.g. a man's hat.

Syllable: A part of a word that can be pronounced separately. A syllable contains one vowel sound. Dismounting has three syllables—dis-mount-ing.

Prefixes: Syllables added at the beginning of a word to affect the meaning of the word. Im + possible means not possible.

Suffixes: Syllables added at the end of a word, e.g. quick + ly meaning in a quick manner.

Vowels: The letters **a**, **e**, **i**, **o**, **u** and sometimes **y**. Vowel sounds written in two letters (**ea**, **ai**) are called vowel digraphs.

Consonants: All the letters of the alphabet except the five vowels are consonants. Two consonants together making one sound are consonant digraphs. **Y** at the beginning of a word is a consonant.

Vowel suffix: A suffix starting with a vowel.

Consonant suffix: A suffix starting with a consonant.

Adding Prefixes

You can make new words by building on to other words. The parts you add at the beginning of a word are called **prefixes**.

In general the spelling of the prefix does not alter, no matter what letter the main word begins with.

Make the following words bigger by adding prefixes. The letter will tell you which prefix to use.

PREFIXES

a. **pre** ... before
b. **mis** ... badly
c. **sub** ... under
d. **re** .... again
e. **dis** .... opposite of
f. **en** .... into
g. **inter** .. between
h. **semi** .. half
i. **over** .. over
j. **under** . under

1. e + appear
2. h + quaver
3. j + ground
4. a + historic
5. c + way
6. i + turn
7. b + use
8. e + continued
9. d + capture
10. j + seal
11. c + normal
12. f + tangled

13. d + fresh
14. g + national
15. i + grown
16. a + fix
17. e + cover
18. g + change
19. d + union
20. h + colon
21. b + understand
22. g + woven
23. a + caution
24. f + closed

5

Ways of Saying Not

There are several different prefixes which are added to words to give them the opposite meaning.

> impossible means not possible
> unhappy   means not   happy

Look what can happen.

> un + necessary ... unnecessary
> im + mature ..... immature

Because the last letter of the prefix is the same as the first letter of the word, you get a double letter.

These prefixes all mean not:

> im   il   in   ir   un

Choose the one you need for each example below. Check the spelling in your check list or dictionary. Notice which ones make double letters.

1. not legible
2. not regular
3. not efficient
4. not probable
5. not certain
6. not resistible
7. not numerable
8. not comfortable
9. not movable
10. not natural
11. not polite
12. not logical

More Prefixes

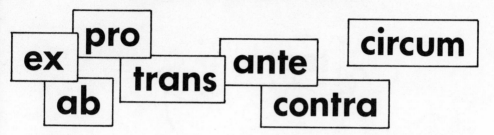

Here are some more useful prefixes. Until now you have added a prefix to a word to make a different word. Many prefixes are added to word parts which are not complete by themselves.

In the first column below you add prefixes to whole words, in the second to word parts. Beside each prefix you are given one common meaning of it.

PREFIXES

a. **ante** ... before
b. **anti** .... against
c. **ab** ..... from
d. **ex** .... out of
e. **trans** .. across
f. **pro** .... before
g. **circum**. around
h. **contra** . against
i. **tele** .... far
j. **tri** ..... three
k. **de** ..... away
l. **super** .. above

1. g + navigate
2. d + change
3. h + diction
4. a + room
5. e + plant
6. i + vision
7. l + human
8. c + original
9. k + rail
10. f + noun
11. b + septic
12. j + angle
13. l + market
14. b + cyclone

15. g + ference
16. k + tached
17. b + dote
18. i + phone
19. e + late
20. c + sence
21. f + gress
22. l + vise
23. h + band
24. j + dent
25. f + ject
26. d + clude
27. e + fer
28. i + gram

ante means before. anti means against.
The prefix **anti** is spelt **ant** before a vowel.

anti + acid . . . . antacid
anti + arctic . . . antarctic

7

Adding Suffixes

A man who plays **cricket** is a **cricketer**. Someone who **teaches** is a **teacher**. Here the suffix **-er** shows the person who does the action.

-ly is a suffix that turns an adjective like **soft** into an adverb **softly**.

Some suffixes, like **-ance** and **-ment** make nouns out of verbs. **Agree** is a verb, **agreement** is a noun.

There are a great many different suffixes, but if you can recognize the common ones it will help you break long words into easy syllables. Make lists of words you find with the same suffixes. Seeing them in groups will help you to remember them.

Look first at words which add a suffix without changing the original word.

SUFFIXES
m. **-er**
n. **-ly**
o. **-ance**
p. **-ment**
q. **-able**

1. build + m
2. assist + o
3. enjoy + p
4. free + n
5. break + q

6. strong + n
7. listen + m
8. disturb + o
9. remark + q
10. move + p

—And More Suffixes

Here is another exercise where you can add the suffix without changing the original word. Spot the ones that produce a double letter.

1. joy + r
2. poet + s
3. differ + v
4. dark + q
5. music + n
6. event + t
7. govern + p
8. hero + w
9. seed + o
10. sudden + q
11. friend + x
12. neighbour + u
13. sail + p
14. haul + m
15. heel + o
16. comic + n
17. hope + t
18. break + m
19. soul + o
20. depend + v
21. mountain + r
22. hard + x
23. child + u
24. post + m
25. patriot + s
26. correspond + v
27. smoke + o
28. instruct + p
29. critic + n
30. magnet + w
31. plain + q
32. exception + n

SUFFIXES

m. **-age**
n. **-al**
o. **-less**
p. **-or**
q. **-ness**
r. **-ous**
s. **-ic**
t. **-ful**
u. **-hood**
v. **-ence**
w. **-ism**
x. **-ship**

Prefixes and Suffixes

You have seen how the meaning and function of a word can be changed by adding a prefix at the beginning of it or a suffix at the end. We can add a prefix and a suffix at the same time, or several of them. From the word **order** you can make **orderly** and **disorderly**. A short word like **truth** can grow into **untruthfulness** (un-truth-ful-ness).

Here are some examples to work. Sometimes the addition of a suffix or prefix can alter the spelling of the original word. This exercise uses only those that leave the word unchanged.

PREFIXES			SUFFIXES	
a.	**un**	1. b + agree + r	m.	**-able**
b.	**dis**	2. g + lead + p	n.	**-ed**
c.	**im**	3. d + pay + r	o.	**-ful**
d.	**re**	4. b + connect + n	p.	**-ing**
e.	**en**	5. a + success + o + q	q.	**-ly**
f.	**in**	6. c + pass + m	r.	**-ment**
g.	**mis**	7. h + port + n	s.	**-less**
h.	**de**	8. fear + s + t	t.	**-ness**
		9. e + large + r		
		10. f + finite + q		

10

When Two Legs are Forelegs

fore means in front, the front part of, or before.

Your *forehead* is the front part of your head. An animal's *forelegs* are the two in front. You *foretell* an event if you tell about it before it happens.

In the following exercise you are given clues to a number of words that begin with *fore*. The endings are jumbled in the box. See if you can think of the words. If you can't, look them up in your dictionary.

arm	1. This tells us what weather to expect.
cast	2. He is in charge of a gang of workmen.
father	3. A feeling that something bad is going to happen.
finger	4. This is the one you point with.
ground	5. The furthest in front—that is, first or best.
warn	6. Your great great-grandfather is one of yours.
shore	7. The morning—before midday.
man	8. The part of the coast nearest the sea.
thought	9. A space in front of a building.
tell	10. Fortune-tellers claim to do this about future events.
boding	11. The part of a landscape nearest the front.
most	12. This is between the hand and the elbow.
noon	13. The ability to think and provide for things before they happen.
court	14. To warn of something before it happens.

Taking Words to Pieces

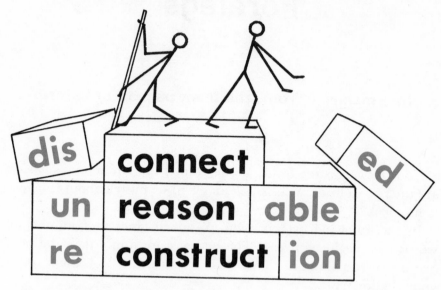

If you find long words difficult to spell, you can break them into syllables. Knowing your prefixes and suffixes will help you to do this.

Say each syllable in turn and spell it. Then put them together as you write the word. Think of the syllables as separate bricks put together.

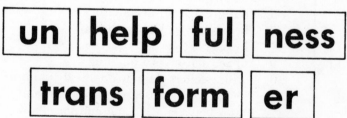

Some of you will find it enough to separate the prefixes and suffixes from the main word. Others may need to break the words into short syllables.

Here are some words that you can take to pieces. They are all quite straightforward. The prefixes and suffixes are all ones you have had.

1. transplanted
2. considerable
3. prevailing
4. abnormally
5. foretelling
6. irregularly
7. forgetfulness
8. dismissal
9. conductor
10. importer
11. disrespectful
12. misunderstood
13. unexpectedly
14. requirement
15. overloaded
16. unprofitable
17. investment
18. outrageous
19. disappearance
20. subtropical

You may Read . . .
You probably Say

—burned the cakes
—dreamed a dream
—kneeled on the floor
—learned his lesson
—spelled a word
—spilled the salt
—spoiled the day
—leaped on a horse

—burnt the cakes
—dreamt a dream
—knelt on the floor
—learnt his lesson
—spelt a word
—spilt the salt
—spoilt the day
—leapt on a horse

Either spelling is correct.

Same Sound, Different Spelling

In the following words the two letters in bold type have the sound of *f*. Read them aloud, and stress the *f*.

toff**ee**   **triump**h   **laug**h**ter**

Complete the unfinished words in the phrases below, putting the correct letters in place of the asterisks. Check your answers.

1. Tra**ic on main roads
2. Answer the tele**one
3. Give a rou** estimate
4. Learning the al**abet
5. The re*eree decides
6. A man with a bad cou**
7. Sti** and bruised
8. A circus ele**ant
9. A di**icult puzzle
10. A tou** bit of meat
11. A friendly dol**in
12. A drau**ty corridor

13. A para**in lamp
14. **ysical training
15. The earth is a s**ere.
16. Turkey with stu**ing
17. Giving his autogra**
18. Lau**ing at a joke
19. A newspaper paragra**
20. Not enou** time
21. On o**icial business
22. An excellent **otogra**
23. In di**erent clothes
24. Feeding from the trou**

No such Word as Glasss!

We make the plural of most nouns by just adding **s**.

hat . . . . hats	chick . . . chicks	nose . . . noses
boy . . . boys	mill . . . . mills	bee . . . . bees

But if we added **s** to glass it would look funny, and we should not be able to hear the difference. So we add **es**.

one glass   two glasses

Nouns ending in hissing sounds like

s sh x z zz

and in **ch** or **tch**

form the plural by adding **es**.
   Try to say bushs, benchs, buzzs and you will see why they are spelt bushes, benches, buzzes.

   Complete the unfinished words in the plural form. Check your answers.

1. Names and addre____
2. Polar bears and walru____
3. Hens eaten by fo____
4. Coats and dre____
5. Weeds and gra____
6. Rates and ta____

7. Princes and prince____
8. All at si____ and sevens
9. Conductors on bu____
10. Clocks and wa____
11. Chapels and chur____
12. Turks wearing fe____

Adding s
to Words that End in y

To form the plural of words that end in **y**, see whether the letter before the **y** is a vowel or a consonant.

If it is a vowel, add **s**.

one day	seven days
one toy	several toys
one monkey	ten monkeys

If it is a consonant, change the **y** into **i** and add **es**.

one baby	five babies
a story	good stories
one party	lots of parties

Following this rule, turn the words in brackets into plurals.

1. (Boy) riding (pony)
2. (Journey) abroad
3. (Supply) of (turkey)
4. Friends and (enemy)
5. (Jockey) in helmets
6. Hills and green (valley)
7. (Baby) playing with (puppy)
8. Luggage on (trolley)
9. (Jelly) and (pastry)
10. In foreign (country)
11. (Sentry) on guard
12. (Stowaway) on ships
13. (County) and (city) of Wales
14. (Lady) on (balcony)
15. Arabs on (donkey)
16. (Gangway) to the boat
17. (Play) about (cowboy)
18. Books from (library)
19. Fishermen in (jersey)
20. Children with (guy)
21. (Factory) with big (chimney)
22. (Birthday) on the same day
23. (Story) about (gipsy)
24. (Lorry) on the (quay)

Adding s to Words that End in

ff   fe   f

Words that end in **ff** take **s**.

cuff ... cuffs   cliff ... cliffs
puff ... puffs   stuff ... stuffs

Words that end in **fe** change the **f** into **v** and add **es**.

wife .... wives   life ... lives
knife ... knives

Some words that end in **f** add **s**.

chief... chiefs   proof ... proofs
roof ... roofs   reef .... reefs

Others change the **f** into **v** and add **es**.

leaf.... leaves   loaf ... loaves
half ... halves   self.... selves

A few can form the plural either way. You may choose:

scarf..... scarfs   or scarves
wharf.... wharfs   or wharves
hoof ..... hoofs   or hooves
dwarf.... dwarfs   or dwarves

The only way of knowing the correct forms of these words is to look them up, use them and learn them. It helps if you say them aloud and listen to the sound.

Adding s
to Words that End in o

There is no rule to tell us whether to add **s** or **es** to these words. They have to be learned.

Some always add **s**.

photo... photos	solo..... solos
piano... pianos	studio... studios

Some always add **es**.

tomato... tomatoes	hero... heroes
potato... potatoes	echo... echoes

A few form the plural with either. You may choose:

Eskimo... Eskimos	or Eskimoes
grotto.... grottos	or grottoes

A good way to remember the spelling is to make nonsense stories or phrases from words of one group, e.g.
with **es**—Cargoes of potatoes and tomatoes
with **s**—Sopranos and contraltos singing solos in studios

Make some for yourselves, but be sure to check the spelling first.

Words ending in **oo** always take **s**.

igloo..... igloos	kangaroo... kangaroos
cuckoo.... cuckoos	tattoo...... tattoos
bamboo... bamboos	zoo........ zoos

18

Revision of Plurals

Following the rules given on pages 15 to 18, put the words in brackets into the plural form. Be sure to check your answers.

I
1. A pack of (wolf)
2. Meat and other (foodstuff)
3. Ships loading at (wharf)
4. A packet of (handkerchief)
5. Wearing long football (scarf)
6. Cows with their (calf)
7. (Thief) and robbers
8. Deserted cottages without (roof)
9. (Shelf) loaded with books
10. Fish living in coral (reef)

II
1. (Cargo) of wheat
2. Electricity from (dynamo)
3. Wallabies and (kangaroo)
4. Lava from (volcano)
5. A collection of (curio)
6. Ships sunk by (torpedo)
7. A game of (domino)
8. A raid by (commando)
9. (Eskimo) in (igloo)
10. Carvings by (Negro)
11. Television (studio)
12. Japanese in (kimono)

III
1. (Prefix) and (suffix)
2. (Pencil) and (brush)
3. A flock of pink (flamingo)
4. (Portfolio) of drawings
5. A clatter of horses' (hoof)
6. Two (half) of an orange
7. (Hobby) for girls
8. (Crate) of (tomato)
9. (Nought) and (cross)
10. (River) with their (tributary)
11. (Boy) playing by (himself)
12. (Race) for (canoe)
13. Narrow (alley) and (entrance)
14. (Box) of (potato) and (carrot)
15. Ripe (strawberry)
16. (Husband) and (wife)
17. (Herd) of (buffalo)
18. (Display) of dancing
19. (Soprano) singing (solo)
20. The whining of (mosquito)

Sh!

Some words are tricky because they begin with silent letters. You could not find them in a dictionary unless you knew what the silent letter would be.

knee	write	gnat	psalm
knot	wrist	gnome	psychic
knit	wrap	gnaw	psychology

In the phrases below, each asterisk stands for one of these silent letters. Complete the words. Check your spelling.

1. *nown for its music
2. *nives and forks
3. Reading and *riting
4. A *rong note
5. A tree *nawed by rabbits
6. She was *neading the bread.
7. The door *nob
8. *nashing his teeth
9. A *notted rope
10. He studied *sychology.
11. The *nu comes from Africa.
12. The *nave of hearts
13. A *ren's nest
14. *rapped in a blanket

15. *neeling by the fire
16. The tadpoles *riggled.
17. Bitten by *nats
18. A *nitted pullover
19. The boat was *recked.
20. A *narled old tree trunk
21. Look at your *ristwatch.
22. He grazed his *nuckles.
23. Goblins and *nomes
24. *rinkled with age
25. *salms and hymns
26. It was a *nockout.
27. General *nowledge
28. Poor *retched man

Sh Again!

Some words have silent letters in the middle or at the end:

b is often silent when it follows **m**

n is silent when it follows **m**

l is often silent before **k**

t is often silent after **s**

Examples of these are:

thumb   autumn   talk   listen

Complete these words. Check your spelling.

1. The yo∗k of an egg
2. The tom∗s of the kings
3. Autum∗ leaves
4. Brush and com∗
5. Singing fo∗k songs
6. A rough tres∗le table
7. Hands num∗ with cold
8. Nettles and this∗les
9. A hym∗ of praise
10. Holly and mis∗letoe
11. Clim∗ed out on a lim∗
12. A Norman cas∗le
13. Ta∗king in your sleep
14. Fas∗en your seatbelt.
15. Add this colum∗ of figures.
16. Deaf and dum∗
17. Flowers with long sta∗ks
18. Use the coloured cha∗k.
19. A bom∗ explosion
20. A cross-country wa∗k
21. Condem∗ed to death
22. Epis∗les of the Apos∗les
23. A plum∗er and his mate
24. My solem∗ promise

Short Vowel—
Long Vowel

It is important to know the difference between a short and a long vowel.

The word **tap** is pronounced with a *short* ă sound.

The word **tape** is pronounced with a *long* ā sound. (The marks ˘ and ¯ are used in dictionaries to show whether a vowel is short or long.)

The **e** at the end of **tape** has no sound itself, but it changes the short ă of **tap** into a long ā. This silent **e** is often called mute **e** because a mute is a person who does not speak.

Silent (or mute) **e** can lengthen other vowels as well as a. Look at these pairs of words. Say them aloud and put the correct mark above the vowel.

mat . . . mate	bit . . . bite	not . . . note
hat . . . . hate	rid . . . ride	rob . . . robe

In the following exercise you are given a clue to the answers. In one part of the answer the vowel has the short sound. In the other it is lengthened by adding mute *e*.

1. *a* It goes on the head
   b A sort of cloak   **ca**

2. *a* Part of a fish
   b Sunny and clear   **fi**

3. *a* Went on horseback
   b Used for fishing   **ro**

4. *a* To tear or slash
   b Ready to be eaten   **ri**

5. *a* To jump on one foot
   b To wish and expect   **ho**

6. *a* An ornamental feather
   b A purple fruit   **plu**

7. *a* A young bear
   b A six-sided figure   **cu**

8. *a* Insane
   b Built or constructed   **ma**

9. *a* A kind of tree
   b It burns   **fi**

10. *a* A space among trees
    b Pleased and happy   **gla**

11. *a* To lose colour
    b A craze   **fa**

12. *a* A scheme
    b A tool for smoothing wood   **pla**

When the words are in pairs as above it is easy to recognize the long vowel and the silent *e*. Try to find them in some of these words:

1. behave
2. suppose
3. magnet
4. complete
5. forsake
6. confuse
7. lemonade
8. respect
9. provide
10. resolute
11. crusade
12. ignite

Doubling the Last Letter

Here is a group of one-syllable words. You will see that each one ends in a single consonant following a single short vowel.

tap   get   hid   hot   rub   skip

When you add a vowel suffix to a word like this, you double the final consonant.

$$t\breve{a}p + ed \ldots\ldots tapped$$
$$g\breve{e}t + ing \ldots\ldots getting$$
$$h\breve{i}d + en \ldots\ldots hidden$$
$$h\breve{o}t + est \ldots\ldots hottest$$
$$r\breve{u}b + er \ldots\ldots rubber$$

When you add a consonant suffix, you do *not* double the final consonant.

$$s\breve{a}d + ness \ldots\ldots sadness$$
$$h\breve{o}t + ly \quad \ldots\ldots hotly$$

Following the rule, add the suffixes shown in brackets to the words below. Remember that you double the consonant only when the suffix begins with a vowel.

1. wet   (-er, -est)
2. rot   (-ed, -en)
3. sad   (-er, -ly)
4. hug   (-ed, -ing)
5. drop   (-ed, -ing)
6. skip   (-ed, -ing)
7. run   (-er, -ing)
8. hat   (-er, -less)
9. net   (-ed, -ing)
10. spot   (-less, -ed)
11. rib   (-ed, -ing)
12. knit   (-ed, -ing)

Note: Words ending in **w**, **x**, **y** do not follow the rule.

Now look at these words:

break   float   droop   haul   cheer   join

The last letter is a single consonant, but it follows a group of two vowels sounded as one (digraph). When you add a suffix the word is not changed.

break + ing . . . . . breaking
float + ed . . . . floated
droop + ing . . . . . drooping
haul + age . . . . . . haulage
cheer + ful . . . . . . cheerful
join + ed . . . . joined

Following the rule, add the suffixes in brackets. It does not matter whether the suffix is a vowel suffix or a consonant suffix.

1. near   (-ly, -est)
2. beat   (-able, -en)
3. feel   (-ing, -ers)
4. soak   (-ed, -ing)
5. dread (-ful, -ed)
6. loud   (-ness, -ly)

7. ail   (-ment, -ing)
8. spoil (-ed, -ing)
9. bear (-ing, -able)
10. cool (-er, -ing)
11. fail (-ed, -ure)
12. greet (-ed, -ing)

Mixed examples. Some have single vowels.

1. cool (-ed, -est)
2. slip (-ed, -ing)
3. big (-er, -est)
4. hear (-ers, -ing)
5. treat (-ed, -ment)
6. hot (-er, -ly)

7. dig (-er, -ing)
8. groan (-ed, -ing)
9. air (-ing, -less)
10. fit (-ness, -ing)
11. steam (-er, -ing)
12. wag (-ing, -ed)

To Double
or Not to Double

Many two-syllable words end with a single consonant following a single short vowel.

As before, the word does not change when you add a consonant suffix.

When you add a vowel suffix, what happens depends on the accent of the word.

ACCENT ON THE **FIRST** SYLLABLE
ONE CONSONANT
Example: The word **orbit** is pronounced ORB-it.
The accent is on the first syllable.
orbit   orbited   orbiting

ACCENT ON THE **SECOND** SYLLABLE
TWO CONSONANTS
Example: The word **admit** is pronounced ad-MIT.
The accent is on the second syllable.
admit   admitted   admitting

Say the word aloud. Add *-ed* and *-ing*.

1. pilot
2. limit
3. profit
4. packet

5. commit
6. allot
7. omit
8. regret

The rule you have just learned applies to the other single consonants except **l**, **x** and **w**. Exceptions are worship, handicap and kidnap.

ACCENT ON THE **FIRST** SYLLABLE
ONE CONSONANT

OR-der	ordered	ordering
GAL-lop	galloped	galloping
FAST-en	fastened	fastening

ACCENT ON THE **SECOND** SYLLABLE
TWO CONSONANTS

be-GIN	beginning	beginner
oc-CUR	occurred	occurrence
dis-BUD	disbudded	disbudding

In the exercise below all the words follow the rule. Add the suffixes in brackets, doubling the consonant where necessary.

1.	alter	(-ed, -ation)	11. happen	(-ed, -ing)
2.	offer	(-ed, -ing)	12. outwit	(-ed, -ing)
3.	prefer	(-ed, -ing)	13. suffer	(-ed, -ing)
4.	listen	(-er, -ing)	14. gossip	(-ed, -ing)
5.	enter	(-ed, -ing)	15. refer	(-ed, -ing)
6.	forget	(-ing, -ful)	16. transmit	(-ing, -er)
7.	hinder	(-ed, -ing)	17. carpet	(-ed, -ing)
8.	recur	(-ed, -ence)	18. chirrup	(-ed, -ing)
9.	differ	(-ing, -ence)	19. acquit	(-ed, -ing)
10.	submit	(-ed, -ing)	20. commit	(-ed, -al)

L is Different

If **l** is the single consonant following a single vowel in a two-syllable word, the accent does not matter. You double the **l** when you add a vowel suffix (except *-ise* or *-ize*). You don't double if you add a consonant suffix.

	Accent on the FIRST syllable Double the **l**		
Example:	TRA-vel	travelled	traveller

	Accent on the SECOND syllable Double the **l**		
Example:	ex-PEL	expelled	expelling

Following the rule, add the suffixes in brackets.

1. quarrel (-ed, -some)
2. compel (-ed, -ing)
3. model (-ed, -ing)
4. travel (-er, -ing)
5. marvel (-ed, -ous)
6. signal (-ed, -man)
7. total (-ed, -ing)
8. cancel (-ed, -ation)
9. excel (-ed, -ent)
10. label (-ed, -ing)
11. appal (-ed, -ing)
12. patrol (-ed, -ing)

There are very few exceptions to this rule. Symbol is one of them. Make a list of any others you find.

When a Consonant Follows a Long Vowel

In the rules for doubling or not doubling the final consonant you have had to ask:

Does the word end in a single consonant?
Does the single consonant come after a single vowel?

Now we look at another group of words where:

The word ends in a single consonant.
The single consonant follows two vowels.
In these words you do not double the consonant.
Examples:

unveil	unveiled	unveiling
remain	remained	remaining
repeat	repeated	repeating

Following the rules you have just learned, complete the unfinished words below by adding *-ed* or *-ing*.

1. They gallop____ off in a cloud of dust.
2. Fifty students enrol____ for the course.
3. The mayor was appeal____ for funds.
4. The men were rivet____ steel plates together.
5. The postman was pedal____ slowly along.
6. The centre forward was transfer____.
7. Napoleon was defeat____ at Waterloo.
8. The club ballot____ for a new president.
9. The men were repair____ the bridge.
10. I am remit____ cash with order.

29

When c is Soft

at the beginning of a word

In most words that begin with **c**, the letter **c** is sounded like **k**. For example, in **cat**, **can**, **cry**, it has the hard sound.

But sometimes the **c** is sounded like **s**. Then we say that it is soft. Soft **c** is usually followed by **i**, **e** or **y**. Here are some examples:

cement   cigarette   cyclist

If you are looking up a word and can't find it under **s**, try looking under **ce**, **ci** or **cy**.

This rule will help you to pronounce difficult new words like cerebral and vicissitude. Check them in your dictionary.

Complete the unfinished words in the phrases below. Remember that although they begin with the sound of **s**, the first letters are **ce**, **ci** or **cy**. See how many there are of each.

1. Clowns in a **rcus
2. Ten **ntimetres long
3. Wrecked in a **clone
4. **ntral heating
5. A barrel of **der
6. Sticks of **lery
7. A **rcular racetrack
8. A swan and her **gnets
9. Lemons are **trus fruit.
10. A marriage **remony
11. Soldiers and **vilians
12. Breakfast **reals
13. The **ntre of a **rcle
14. **linders of gas
15. To **lebrate the victory
16. Cloves and **nnamon
17. Sad **press trees
18. A **rtain remedy
19. A **tizen of London
20. In the twentieth **ntury
21. Smoking a fat **gar
22. With a **nical laugh
23. Drums and **mbals
24. Television **lebrities

—and in the middle of a word.

You have seen that words sometimes begin with the letter **c** though they sound as if they begin with **s**.

The same thing can be found in other parts of a word. Again this happens when the next letter is **e, i** or **y**.

recent   council   mercy

Complete the unfinished words in the phrases below. The asterisks stand for **ce, ci** or **cy**, and the **c** is sounded as **s**.

1. A par**l of books
2. A con**rt pianist
3. Re**ting poetry
4. A jui** pear
5. To can**l the order
6. Heated by electri**ty
7. A magnifi**nt palace
8. Knitting a la** pattern
9. Pen**l and paper
10. An inno**nt victim
11. The prin**pal of the college
12. A huge en**clopaedia
13. A fan** dress parade
14. He arrived re**ntly.
15. A vacan** for a typist
16. An in**ssant hum of bees
17. This butter is ran**d.
18. Flee** white clouds
19. De**ding the route
20. A con**ntrated essence
21. De**mal curren**
22. Spi** smell of nutmeg
23. A re**pe for doughnuts
24. A spe**men of moon rock

Watch for soft **c** when it follows **s** if the next letter is **i, e** or **y**.

science   descend   Scilly   scene   scissors
scythe

Watch for soft **c** when it follows a hard **c** before **i, e** or **y**.

accent   accelerate   accept   access
accident   eccentric   occident

Watch for soft **c** when it follows **ex** before **i** or **e**.

exceed   excel   excellent   except   excite

When e is Silent

What happens when you add a suffix to a word ending in silent (mute) **e**?

The rule is clear, and it almost always applies.

When you add a consonant suffix to a word ending in silent **e**, you leave the word unchanged.

hope + ful . . . . . . hopeful

amuse + ment . . . amusement

When you add a vowel suffix to a word ending in silent **e**, you drop the silent **e**.

hope + ing . . . . . hoping

amuse + ed . . . . amused

Adding vowel suffixes: follow the rule.
Add *-ing* to the words below.

1. drive	6. advise	11. owe
2. please	7. bite	12. leave
3. move	8. come	13. provide
4. shake	9. give	14. ache
5. taste	10. smile	15. vote

Add *-ed* to the words below.

1. praise	6. race	11. surprise
2. choke	7. tire	12. suppose
3. dance	8. curve	13. blaze
4. save	9. wave	14. dine
5. smoke	10. serve	15. sneeze

Adding consonant suffixes: follow the rule.

1. white + ness	6. love + ly
2. like + ness	7. precise + ly
3. strange + ness	8. live + ly
4. late + ness	9. sincere + ly
5. forgive + ness	10. nice + ly

Adding mixed suffixes.

1. advertise (-ment, -ing)	9. admire (-ation, -er)
2. wake (-ful, -ing)	10. compete (-ing, -ed)
3. invite (-ation, -ed)	11. arrange (-ment, -ing)
4. use (-ing, -able)	12. receive (-er, -ing)
5. like (-ly, -ing)	13. waste (-ful, -ed)
6. arrive (-al, -ed)	14. encourage (-ing, -ment)
7. explore (-ing, -ation)	15. rule (-er, -ing)
8. starve (-ation, -ing)	16. confuse (-ing, -ion)

If you find any exceptions to the rule, first check them in a dictionary, then list them in a notebook. Try to remember them. **Mileage, ageing** and **changeable** are exceptions.

Same Sound, Different Spelling

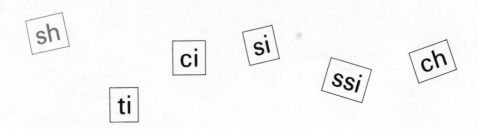

In the following words the letters in bold type all have the sound of **sh**. Read the words aloud and stress the **sh**.

stati**on**   mu**si**c**ian**   dimen**si**on   se**ssi**on   **ch**ivalry

Complete the unfinished words in the phrases below, putting the correct letters in place of the asterisks. Check your answers.

1. A noisy ma**ine
2. In an upright posi**on
3. Artifi**al flowers
4. Cheap excur**on tickets
5. A sulky expre***on
6. Dropped by para**ute
7. Addi**on and subtrac**on
8. An exten**on to the house
9. Deli**ous strawberries
10. A **alet in the Alps
11. A collec**on of coins
12. A commer**al college
13. Permi***on to leave
14. Sold by auc**on
15. A bottle of **ampagne
16. In the wrong direc**on
17. An an**ent monument
18. A spe**al attrac**on
19. In posse***on of stolen goods
20. The dimen**ons of the room
21. The so**al services
22. A proce***on of old cars
23. An invita**on to a party
24. A retirement pen**on

Easy!

Something you do with **ease** is **easy**.

An orange with plenty of **juice** is **juicy**.

Ease and juice end in mute **e** after a single consonant. **-y** is a vowel suffix, so we drop the silent **e** before adding **-y**.

Make words ending in **-y** to describe these things:

1. Buttons that shine are . . . . . .
2. Pastry that is in thin flakes is . . . . . .
3. Snails covered in slime are . . . . . .
4. A wind as cold as ice is . . . . . .
5. A machine making a lot of noise is . . . . . .
6. Fingers covered with grease are . . . . . .
7. A corner exposed to the breeze is . . . . . .
8. A place in the shade is . . . . . .

Beware of fire!

The adjective is **fiery**.

35

ie or ei?

Most of you have heard the rhyme

i before e except after c.

This is probably the easiest way of remembering the rule. However it does not tell you all that is necessary. The rule applies only to syllables that rhyme with bee. So the following rhyme could be used instead:

When these letters rhyme with bee
Put i before e except after c.

Note: The rule does not apply to names like Keith, Sheila, Deirdre, Neil.

p**ce (of paper) The ** rhymes with bee. It is spelt **ie**.	rec**ve (a gift) The ** rhymes with bee, but it comes after **c**. It is spelt **ei**.
field priest brief siege niece relieve	deceit conceited ceiling deceived receipt perceive

An important exception is

seize.

Other exceptions are **weird, counterfeit**.

ie or ei?

Remember the rhyme.

Following the rule, complete the unfinished words.

1. Stop, th**f!
2. A br**f letter
3. With sword and sh**ld
4. Overcome with gr**f
5. To rel**ve the pain
6. Conc**ted about her singing
7. The parish pr**st
8. Howling like f**nds

9. To ach**ve success
10. A rec**pt for the money
11. Fishing from the p**r
12. A p**rcing shr**k
13. Spaniels and retr**vers
14. A bes**ged city
15. A good y**ld of wheat
16. My n**ce, Rosemary

All the examples so far have had the sound **ee**. But many syllables containing **ei** rhyme with day.

holding the r**ns
The ** does not rhyme with bee.
It does not belong to the rule.

weight   sleigh
leisure   forfeit

1. The horse n**ghed.
2. A beetle f**gns death.
3. The r**gn of King John
4. Hidden behind a v**l
5. A fr**ght train

6. V**ns and arteries
7. R**ndeer and sledges
8. Cows and h**fers
9. Sk**ns of wool
10. In for**gn lands

37

Same Sound, Different Spelling

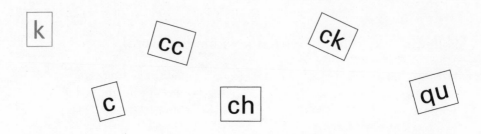

In the following words the letters in bold type all have the sound of **k**. Read them aloud, and stress the **k**.

magic accused chaos socket opaque

Complete the unfinished words in the phrases below, putting the correct letters in place of the asterisks. Check your answers.

1. A bro*en an*le
2. Bitten by mos**itoes
3. A pa**et of crisps
4. The announcer's mi*rophone
5. Severe stoma** a**e
6. A**ording to the rules
7. Medicine from the **emist
8. Anti**e furniture
9. A strange o**urrence
10. An ele*tri* *ettle
11. Designed by an ar**itect
12. Keep a**urate a**ounts
13. Bla** woollen sto**ings
14. Motorway traffi*
15. The burglar's a**omplice
16. A che**e for £10
17. A splendid o**asion
18. Un*les and aunts
19. A surprise atta**
20. A motor me**ani*
21. Plum and peach *ernels
22. A man of good **aracter
23. The Ar*ti* Ocean
24. In the ba**ground

Disappearing Letters

A man who acts is an actor, but a woman who acts is an actress actor + ess (without the o).

Generous people are known for their generosity (without the u).

To complete the sentences below, put in a word formed from the word underlined. In each case a letter is dropped.

1. A female tiger is a _____.
2. Enter the building through the side _____.
3. In winter we expect _____ weather.
4. Things that hinder us are a _____.
5. The way to pronounce a word is called its _____.
6. Flashes that lighten the sky in a storm are called _____.
7. An actress known for her glamour is called _____.
8. A boy with plenty of vigour is _____.
9. A carpenter is expert in _____.
10. A Negro woman is a _____.
11. When we exclaim we make an _____.
12. If you repeat a thing often you learn by _____.
13. A boiler shaped like a cylinder is a _____ boiler.
14. They proclaim the new king by issuing a _____.
15. When liquids turn into vapour they _____.
16. A story full of humour is a _____ story.

39

When g is Soft it Sounds Like j

When **g** is followed by **e**, **i** or **y** it is often sounded like **j**. You must remember to spell it **g**. Here are some examples.

giant	geometry	gymnasium
giraffe	general	gyroscope

Complete the unfinished words in the phrases below. Remember that the asterisks stand for **ge**, **gi** or **gy**.

1. Ladies and **ntlemen
2. Diseases carried by **rms
3. A **psy caravan
4. **nuine antiques
5. A display by **mnasts
6. A **nerous gift
7. A **ngerbread man
8. A **gantic statue
9. Masculine **nder
10. Riding in the **mkhana
11. Zebras and **raffes
12. The **ography lesson
13. An electricity **nerator
14. **ants and ogres
15. The **rmination of seeds
16. A **nius at mathematics
17. A **sture of despair
18. Hanging on a **bbet
19. A hoard of precious **ms
20. Training in a **mnasium

There are about 20 common words beginning **gi** where **g** has the normal hard sound, and far fewer beginning **ge**. Look them up in your dictionary. Here are a few examples.

gear	get	geese	gelding	geyser
girdle	give	gift	gimlet	giddy

40

Not Only at the Beginning

You have seen how **g** can often be sounded like **j** at the beginning of a word. This can happen just as well in other positions. Again **g** is usually followed by **e**, **i** or **y**.

Some examples are:

margin   engine   algebra   change   energy   biology

Complete the unfinished words in the phrases below. The asterisks stand for **ge**, **gi** or **gy**.

1. A doctor's sur**ry
2. Breathing in oxy**n
3. Pain from indi**stion
4. Diesel en**nes
5. Apolo**es for lateness
6. An intelli**nt dog
7. Chan**able weather
8. A re**ment of soldiers
9. Dark and din**
10. King's Colle**
11. Ima**ne the scene
12. Names on a re**ster

13. A racing pi**on
14. Le**nds and stories
15. Latitude and lon**tude
16. Equatorial re**ons
17. Soaps and deter**nts
18. Dancing with a**lity
19. Travel a**ncies
20. Comedy and tra**dy
21. Aller**c to cheese
22. Dates and tan**rines
23. Too stin** to pay
24. The Roman le**ons

Traps and Pitfalls

He is also a scout.
Have you finished already?
We always do this.
It is altogether too difficult.
He almost fell.

They were all so happy.
Are you all ready to go?
These are all ways to town.
We found them all together.
They were all most helpful.

BUT: He said it was **all right**.
　　All right is never made into one word.

41

Numbers in Words

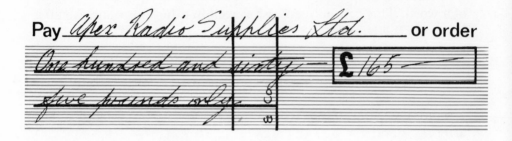

Pay _Apex Radio Supplies Ltd._ ____ or order

One hundred and sixty — five pounds only.   £ 165

There are times when you must write numbers in words. On a cheque you put the amount in figures (£10) and also in words (ten pounds). In legal documents the dates have to be set out in words: The twenty-seventh day of May One thousand nine hundred and seventy-four.

Some numbers are easy to spell, but are you sure you can write 48 correctly in words? Remember these points.

There is a **U** in	but not in
four (fourth)	forty (fortieth)
fourteen	

There is an **E** in	but not in
nine	ninth
nineteen (nineteenth)	
ninety (ninetieth)	

There is a **V** in	but an **F** in
five	fifth
	fifteen (fifteenth)
	fifty (fiftieth)
There is a **V** in	but an **F** in
twelve	twelfth

The numbers twenty to ninety take a hyphen before the units number. The others do not.

twenty-four   forty-six   two hundred and six

Write these numbers in words. Check the spelling. Have you put hyphens where they are needed?

1. 4, 14, 40, 44, 48, 84
2. 5, 50, 55th, 15, 15th
3. 8, 8th, 18, 18th, 80, 80th, 88th
4. 9, 9th, 19, 90, 90th, 99th
5. 12, 12th
6. 20th, 30th, 60th, 70th
7. 51, 51st, 42, 42nd, 33, 33rd

 Remember eight + th . . . eighth

Who is the Owner?

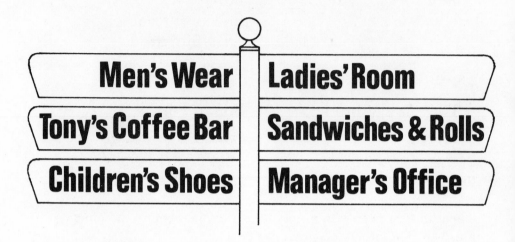

An apostrophe is used to show the owner (or user) of a thing. In the signs above, read the word before the apostrophe. It will answer the question at the top of the page. The coffee bar belongs to Tony. The shoes are for children. Sandwiches and rolls do not have an apostrophe because they don't own anything.

When you want to show the owner or user of anything,
1. Write the word.
2. Put an apostrophe after the word.
3. Add an **s** if you need it for the sound.

A dress belonging to Mary .... is Mary's dress.
A corner for pets .... is pets' corner.
Books for children .... are children's books.
A dog belonging to Mr Jones .... is Mr Jones's dog.
The violin belonging to Sherlock Holmes .. is Sherlock Holmes's violin.

For the following exercise rule two columns. Label the first one *Owner* and the second *Thing Owned*.

Owner	Thing Owned
1. The Boys	Brigade
2. The baker	shop

The answers to the first two examples have been given above. Remember that the apostrophe comes immediately after the name of the owner. Use this clue to help you.

1. The Boys' Brigade
2. The baker's shop
3. The kangaroo's tail
4. The milkman's round
5. The men's ward
6. Sparrows' nests
7. Babies' bottles
8. Dad's chair
9. Pirates' chests
10. Children's library
11. The Indian's pony
12. The Indians' hunting ground

Although we use the terms *Owner* and *Thing Owned* for convenience, some possessives could be expressed more accurately. For example:

An old people's outing   is an outing for old people.
A ladies' restroom   is a restroom for the use of ladies.
St James's Square   is a square named after St James.
Someone's umbrella   is an umbrella belonging to someone.

More difficult examples are:
A day's holiday   is a holiday for the period of a day.
A term's work   is work for the period of a term.
Five years' imprisonment   is imprisonment for the period of five years.

Rearrange the following phrases so that the owner is put first. Put the apostrophe after the owner. Add an **s** if you need one.

1. *a* Crops belonging to the farmer
   b Crops grown by farmers
2. *a* The bicycle owned by David
   b The bicycles belonging to the girls
3. *a* The study used by the Headmaster
   b The day for honouring mothers
4. *a* A bone for the dog
   b Entrance for out-patients
5. *a* The claws of a bear
   b A picnic for teddy bears
6. *a* A jacket for a man
   b A handbag made for a lady
7. *a* The tools belonging to the workmen
   b The church dedicated to St Peter
8. *a* Lime juice made by Mr Rose
   b The hut used by the scouts
9. *a* The singles final for women
   b The story told by the old woman
10. *a* A holiday lasting a week
    b A holiday lasting six weeks

FOR SALE
POTATOES 6p per bag
MARROWS 3 for 10p.

These are ordinary plurals, not possessives. There is no apostrophe.

The apostrophe showing ownership is used only for nouns.

hers mine theirs ours his yours whose

These are not nouns. They do not take any apostrophe. They are called possessive pronouns because they themselves show ownership.

Whose book? Mary's book, or just Mary's.
Is it their book? No, it is ours.
Is this yours or mine? Neither. It is theirs.
Yours affectionately.   Yours sincerely.
This room is his. That is hers.

Put in the missing word.

1. It belongs to them. It is _____.
2. It belongs to Father. It is _____.
3. A book belonging to Tom is _____ book.
4. A discovery made by Columbus is _____ discovery.
5. It belongs to her. It is _____.
6. A cathedral named after St Paul is St _____ Cathedral.
7. A hospital named after St Thomas is St _____ Hospital.
8. A school for girls is a _____ school.
9. A race for beginners is a _____ race.
10. A horse owned by a cowboy is a _____ horse.
11. Saddles used by cowboys are _____ saddles.
12. Work done by cowboys is _____ work.

47

y or i?

Look at these words:

play   obey   enjoy   buy

Each one ends with **y**, and the letter before the **y** is a vowel. Consonant or vowel suffixes can be added without changing the **y**.

A   playful   obeyed   enjoyment   buying

Look at these words:

apply   empty   marry   copy

Each one ends with **y**, but the letter before the **y** is a consonant. Change the **y** into **i** before adding a suffix.

B   appliance   emptiness   marriage   copied

unless the suffix begins with **i**. (You don't want two **i**'s together.)

C   applying   emptying   marrying   copying

Look at the completed word and say if it is like **A**, **B** or **C**.

1. play + ful . . . . playful   **A**
2. satisfy + ing . . . . satisfying
3. beauty + ful . . . . beautiful
4. carry + age . . . . carriage
5. buoy + ant . . . . buoyant
6. fly + ing . . . . flying
7. forty + eth . . . . fortieth
8. disobey + ing . . . . disobeying

48

y or i?

Using the rules you have just learnt, finish the words in the sentences below. The word in brackets is your clue.

1. The carr*er brought the parcel.   (carry)
   It was sent 'carr*age paid'.
   She was carr*ing a heavy basket.
2. Germany and Russia were all*es.   (ally)
   But Germany broke the all*ance.
   England was all*ed with France.
3. The dog was bur*ing a bone.   (bury)
   He bur*ed it in the garden.
   He bur*es everything there.
4. They empt*ed the tank.   (empty)
   The empt*ness increased the noise.
   They spent a whole day empt*ing it.
5. The children worked on bus*ly.   (busy)
   The man owned a furniture bus*ness.
6. They surve*ed the miserable prospect.   (survey)
   A team of men surve*ing the district.

' Stands for Something

In a letter you may write 'I am sorry I cannot come', but if you were speaking to your friend you would probably say 'I'm sorry I can't come'.

These shortened words are used in talking, but not usually in business letters or serious writing.

When a word is shortened in this way we use an apostrophe to show that something has been left out.

I'm is short for **I am**. The apostrophe stands for **a**.
I've is short for **I have**. The apostrophe stands for **ha**.
I can't is short for **I cannot**. The apostrophe stands for **no**.

The apostrophe must be put just where the missing letters should be.

shall not is shortened to **shan't** (not sha'n't)
will not is shortened to **won't**
(will was once spelt 'wol'.)

50

Missing Letters

Use the apostrophe to replace one letter.

1. He is	9. Did not
2. We are	10. Must not
3. They are	11. Does not
4. Who is	12. Is not
5. Where is	13. Do not
6. What is	14. Are not
7. There is	15. Have not
8. How is	16. Could not

Use the apostrophe to replace two letters.

1. I have	9. What has
2. You have	10. What will
3. You will	11. There have
4. He will	12. There will
5. It will	13. How have
6. We have	14. Can not
7. They have	15. Who has
8. They will	16. Who will

Use the apostrophe to replace three letters.

1. I shall	2. We shall

Use the apostrophe to replace four letters.

1. I would	4. Who would
2. You would	5. They would
3. She would	6. There would

Use the apostrophe to replace five letters.

1. I should	2. We should

Its or It's?

Which do you mean?

Its means **belonging to it.**

This word is not a noun, so it does not take an apostrophe. It is a possessive adjective like his, our, your, their. Only nouns have an apostrophe to show ownership.

| your hand | their home | the bird's wing |
| the king's hand | its home | its wing |

It's means **it is.**

The apostrophe stands for the missing letter **i.**

| It's a fine day. | It's yours. | It's hot. |
| It's time to go. | It's my turn. | It's late. |

In the same way,

Whose means **belonging to whom.**

Again this word shows ownership, but it is not a noun. It has no apostrophe.

| Whose turn is it? | The girl whose leg |
| Whose book is this? | was broken. |

Who's means **who is.**

The apostrophe stands for the missing letter **i.**

| Who's coming? | Who's there? |

Air- or Aer- ?
Aircraft but Aeroplanes

Words concerning the air vary in spelling. There is no rule to help you, but if **o** is the next letter, the spelling is usually **aer**. Most new words follow the American style and use **air**.

Look carefully at these lists of examples and try to learn them.

aeroplane	aircraft
aerodrome	airfield
aerobatics	aircrew
aerodynamics	airborne
aeronautical	airmail
aerosol	airline
aeronautics	airtight
also	airworthy
aerated	airstrip
aerial	airport
	airship
	airway
	airspeed *and many more.*

Complete the unfinished words in the phrases below. Put **aer** or **air** in place of the asterisks. Check your answers from the lists above.

1. Landing at the ***port
2. A military ***odrome
3. An ***tight jar
4. A television ***ial
5. A display of ***obatics
6. Sprayed from an ***osol
7. ***mail letters
8. Travelling by ***oplane
9. Balloons and ***ships
10. ***borne seeds
11. The study of ***onautics
12. An aquarium must be ***ated.
13. Anti-***craft guns
14. A map showing ***ways
15. Passengers and ***crew
16. The enemy bombed the ***strip.

Dropping an I

Someone who is *full of hope* is *hopeful* (with only one **l**). Something that makes you *full of pity* is *pitiful*. 'Pity' ends in **y** after a consonant. Change **y** into **i** before you add the suffix **-ful**.

You will see from the exercise that the suffix **-ful** does not always mean precisely 'full of'; but the spelling follows the rule.

Put in the missing words. The word in brackets is your clue.

1. Be _____ with that dish.   (care)
2. Aeroplanes need _____ engines.   (power)
3. Apples are _____ this year.   (plenty)
4. It was a _____ opportunity.   (wonder)
5. She measured it _____ by _____.   (spoon)
6. This is a very _____ tool.   (use)
7. Remind him; he is so _____.   (forget)

Notice that if you add the suffix **-ly** to these words, you get
hopeful + ly . . . hopefully   pitiful + ly . . . pitifully

l is sometimes dropped in the middle of a word. There is no special rule to help you here. Keep a list of those you find, and revise them from time to time.

Here are some examples:

skilful   belfry
wilful   welcome
chilblain   welfare

Look back also to page 41.

Tricky Words

In the phrases below points worth special notice are marked. Learn these tricky words. It is worth keeping a list of them handy for revision. Add other tricky words you come across.

Set I
1. A woollen scarf
2. Raspberry jam
3. A packet of biscuits
4. An independent opinion
5. Attached by strings
6. A cup of cocoa
7. To recommend a book
8. Presents bought at a bazaar
9. Roast chestnuts
10. Stolen by a burglar
11. A bottle of medicine
12. Reading and arithmetic
13. An impromptu speech
14. Holidays abroad

Set II
1. The date on the calendar
2. Sweets and chocolates
3. Houses of Parliament
4. A septic toe
5. A caterpillar tractor
6. Aspirin for a headache
7. Peanuts and walnuts
8. No heavy vehicles
9. To withhold consent
10. Ploughs and other implements
11. An exhibition of paintings
12. Stairs without banisters
13. A colossal statue
14. The island of Majorca

Prefixes and Suffixes
but not so easy

In previous exercises you have added prefixes and suffixes without having to change the original words.

In the following exercise each word will have to be changed according to one of three rules you have learnt about:

A Dropping the mute **e** before adding a vowel suffix.

starve + ation . . . starvation

(see page 32)

B Changing **y** into **i** before adding a suffix.

reply + ed . . . replied

(see page 48)

C Doubling the final consonant before a vowel suffix in the appropriate words.

submit + ing . . . submitting

(see pages 26–29)

PREFIXES		SUFFIXES
a. **con**	1. h + happy + s	m. **-able**
b. **dis**	2. g + fit + p	n. **-age**
c. **em**	3. d + courage + q	o. **-al**
d. **en**	4. h + steady + r	p. **-ed**
e. **in**	5. confer + q	q. **-ing**
f. **mis**	6. e + cure + m	r. **-ly**
g. **re**	7. f + carry + n	s. **-ness**
h. **un**	8. g + arrange + q	
i. **im**	9. h + wrap + q	
	10. e + vary + m	
	11. h + believe + m	
	12. b + approve + o	
	13. c + bed + p	
	14. b + satisfy + p	
	15. i + move + m	
	16. h + occupy + p	

An extra k —

When you **ice** a cake, you
put **icing** on it.
But when you have a **picnic**
you are **picnicking**.
The extra **k** tells you it does not rhyme with **icing**.
   panic   traffic   mimic   frolic   are like picnic.
They take an extra **k** before *-ed* and *-ing*.

Saying and Spelling

Words are often spelt wrongly because they are said wrongly. For instance a tool for pulling out nails is called 'pinchers' instead of the correct 'pincers'.

Here are some well-known trouble-makers. Look hard at the syllables and say them aloud. Do you always pronounce them correctly?

Feb-**ru**-ary   (pronounced Feb'-roo-ary)
rec-**og**-nize   (pronounced reck'-og-nize)
mis-chiev-**ous**   (pronounced mis'-chiv-us)
arc-tic   (pronounced arc'-tic)

With the help of a dictionary, complete the words below.

1. **Lib**_____: a collection of books on shelves. (This word has three syllables—watch the next letter.)
2. **Panto**_____: a comical stage show with singing and dancing. (There is no *n* in the last syllable.)
3. **Asph**_____: a kind of smooth black paving material. (The first syllable is not *ash*. The second syllable has no *e*.)
4. **Vet**_____: concerning the medical treatment of animals. (The next syllable is not *in*.)
5. **Ane**_____: the wild windflowers or red and blue garden flowers. (The next letter is not *n*.)
6. **Itin**_____: a route or plan of travel. (Three more syllables are needed.)
7. **Diph**_____: a dangerous disease of the throat. (The first syllable is pronounced *dif* not *dip*.)
8. **Contem**_____: belonging to the same period of time. (Three more syllables are needed.)

S for a Verb

Some words are spelt with **s** when they are verbs, but **c** when they are nouns.

s for a verb	**c** for a noun
You license a dog	by getting a dog licence.
You must practise kicking goals	so you go to football practice.
When you advise someone .	you give him advice.

If you can't remember
which is which,
Send for the **C**rocodile!
(verb)   (noun)

Traps and Pitfalls

liqu
stup   **id**
putr

liqu
stup   **efied**
putr

Brit
ain is the country.
ons are the people.
annia is the symbol.
ish people live there.

59

More Tricky Words

In the phrases below points worth special notice are marked. Learn these tricky words and be ready to spell them if you have a spelling quiz.

Set I
1. **In**oculated with serum
2. An extra**o**rdinary idea
3. De**sicc**ated coconut
4. Lunch in a rest**au**rant
5. As a special priv**ileg**e
6. A painful ab**scess**
7. F**luo**res**c**ent lighting
8. Feeling shy and emba**rrass**ed
9. P**a**ra**lle**l lines
10. To rec**og**nize a tune
11. The Ist**h**mus of Panama
12. An ostri**ch** feather

Set II
1. An **i**cicle melting
2. Marg**a**rine or butter
3. A naval **lieu**tenant
4. A pair of sharp s**c**issors
5. A sate**ll**ite in space
6. The next instal**m**ent
7. A bus **queue**
8. Highly infla**mm**able
9. Mi**sc**ellaneous examples
10. A penici**ll**in injection
11. Turning a som**ers**a**ult**
12. Stewed r**h**ubarb

There's a rat in separate!

sep e

CHECK LIST

In working the exercises, pupils may use this list to check those spellings that are not self-evident from the context. The full vocabulary range of the book is considerably wider than is shown here.

accomplice
according
accounts
accurate
ache
achieve
aching
acquitted
acquitting
addition
addresses
admiration
admirer
advertisement
advertising
advising
agencies
agility
ailing
ailment
airing
airless
allergic
alleys
alliance
allied
allies
allotted
allotting
alphabet
alteration
altered
ancient
anemone

ankle
antique
apologies
Apostles
appalled
appalling
appealing
architect
Arctic
aren't
arrangement
arranging
arrival
arrived
artificial
asphalt
attack
attraction
auction
autograph
autumn

babies
background
balconies
balloted
bearable
bearing
beatable
beaten
beautiful
besieged

bigger
biggest
birthdays
biting
black
blazed
bomb
boxes
boys
breezy
brief
broken
brushes
buffaloes
buried
buries
burying
buses
busily
business

calves
cancel
cancellation
cancelled
canoes
can't
cap, cape
careful
cargoes
carpentry
carpeted
carpeting

carriage
carrier
carrots
carrying
castle
celebrate
celebrities
celery
centimetres
central
centre
century
cereals
ceremony
certain
chalet
chalk
champagne
changeable
character
chemist
cheque
chimneys
chirruped
chirruping
choked
churches
cider
cigar
cinnamon
circle
circular
circus
cities

citizen
citrus
civilians
climbed
coats
collection
college
column
comb
coming
commandos
commercial
committal
committed
committing
compelled
compelling
competed
competing
conceited
concentrated
concert
condemned
conferring
confusing
confusion
contemporary
cooled
cooler
coolest
cooling
cough
couldn't
counties
countries
cowboys
crates
crosses
cub, cube
curios
currency

curved
cyclone
cygnets
cylinders
cylindrical
cymbals
cynical
cypress

danced
deciding
decimal
defeated
delicious
detergents
didn't
difference
different
differing
difficult
digger
digging
dimensions
dined
dingy
diphtheria
direction
disapproval
displays
dissatisfied
doesn't
dolphin
dominoes
donkeys
don't
draughty
dreaded
dreadful
dresses
driving

dropped
dropping
dumb
dynamos

eight
eighteen
eighteenth
eighth
eightieth
eighty
eighty-eighth
eighty-four
electric
electricity
elephant
elves
embedded
emptied
emptiness
emptying
encouragement
encouraging
encyclopaedia
enemies
engines
enough
enrolled
entered
entering
entrance
entrances
epistles
Eskimo(e)s
excelled
excellent
exclamation
excursion
exploration
exploring

expression
extension

factories
fad, fade
failed
failure
fancy
fasten
feelers
feeling
feigns
fezes
fiends
fifteen
fifteenth
fifty
fifty-fifth
fifty-first
fifty-one
fin, fine
fir, fire
fitness
fitting
five
flaky
flamingos
fleecy
folk
foods
foodstuffs
foreign
forgetful
forgetting
forgiveness
forty
forty-eight
forty-four
forty-second
forty-two

four
fourteen
foxes
freight

galloped
gangways
gems
gender
generator
generous
genius
gentlemen
genuine
geography
germination
germs
gesture
giants
gibbet
gigantic
gingerbread
gipsies
gipsy
giraffes
giving
glad, glade
glamorous
gnarled
gnashing
gnats
gnawed
gnomes
gnu
gossiped
gossiping
grasses
greasy
greeted
greeting
grief

groaned
groaning
guys
gymkhana
gymnasium
gymnasts

halves
handkerchiefs
happened
happening
hatless
hatter
haven't
hearers
hearing
heifers
he'll
herds
he's
hindered
hindering
hindrance
hobbies
hoofs or hooves
hop, hope
hotly
hotter
how's
how've
hugged
hugging
humorous
husbands
hymn

icy
I'd
igloos
I'll
illegible

illogical
imagine
immovable
impolite
improbable
incessant
incurable
indigestion
inefficient
innocent
innumerable
intelligent
invariable
invitation
invited
irregular
irresistible
isn't
itinerary
it'll
I've

jellies
jerseys
jockeys
journeys
juicy

kangaroos
kernels
kettle
kimonos
knave
kneading
kneeling
knitted
knitting
knives
knob
knockout
knotted

knowledge
known
knuckles

labelled
labelling
lace
lacy
ladies
lateness
laughing
leaving
legends
legions
libraries
library
lightning
likely
likeness
liking
limb
limited
limiting
listener
listening
lively
longitude
lorries
loudly
loudness
lovely

machine
mad, made
magnificent
marvelled
marvellous
mechanic
merciful
microphone
miscarriage

mistletoe
modelled
modelling
mosquitoes
moving
mustn't

nearest
nearly
Negress
Negroes
neighed
netted
netting
nicely
niece
nine
nineteen
ninetieth
ninety
ninety-ninth
ninth
noisy
noughts
numb

occasion
occurrence
offered
offering
official
omitted
omitting
outwitted
outwitting
owing
oxygen

packet
packeted

packeting
pantomime
parachute
paraffin
paragraph
parcel
pastries
patrolled
patrolling
pedalling
pencil
pencils
pension
permission
photograph
physical
pier
piercing
pigeon
piloted
piloting
plan, plane
plays
pleasing
plentiful
plum, plume
plumber
ponies
portfolios
position
possession
potatoes
powerful
praised
precisely
preferred
preferring
prefixes
priest
princesses
principal

procession
proclamation
profited
profiting
pronunciation
providing
psalms
psychology
puffs
puppies

quarrelled
quarrelsome
quays

raced
races
rancid
rearranging
receipt
receiver
receiving
recently
recipe
reciting
recurred
recurrence
reefs
referee
referred
referring
refitted
regiment
regions
regretted
regretting
register
reign
reindeer
relieve

remitting
repairing
repetition
retrievers
ribbed
ribbing
rip, ripe
rivers
riveting
rod, rode
roofs
rotted
rotten
rough
ruler
ruling
runner
running

sadder
sadly
saved
scarfs, scarves
sentries
served
seventieth
shady
shaking
she'd
shelves
shield
shiny
shriek
signalled
signaller
sincerely
sixes
sixtieth
skeins
skipped